THE MUSICAL RAINBOW STORY
Donald Abrams

Rainbow Wizard Press, California, USA

Illustrators: Joyce Linda Sfregola (Front Cover, Back Cover, pgs. 30, 32-34, 40), all others Kelly McMahon
Story Text Editor: Carol Sperling   Book Designers: J.P.Van Gordon and Gwen Gades
Contributors: Phyllis Fowler, Amanda Krugh   Happy Birthday Song by Patty Hill & Mildred J. Hill (Public Domain)

Library of Congress PCN 2016946219   ISBN 978-0-9977400-0-4   First Edition 2016

Website: TheMusicalRainbowStory.com has a Demonstration Video, Free Coloring Book Page, & More Free Fun Stuff

MW00934033

Once upon a time, a boy named Peter sat at his piano, day after day, trying to read the music notes to play the "Happy Birthday" song. This day, Saturday, would be Suzy's ninth birthday and Peter had promised to play the song for her birthday party.

Saturday had rolled around all too quickly. Peter woke up to a gloomy, rainy morning. He was determined to try again to read the music notes. He sat down at the old piano and stared at those black and white keys. He tried to play the song but most of the notes he played were wrong.

Finally, his mother came in and said, "Peter, why don't you take a break for lunch? It's almost time to get ready to go to Suzy's party."

"I'm not hungry, Mom," said Peter. He was so frustrated! Maybe he could find a way to stay home from the party.

"Why don't you go to your room and rest?" his mother suggested. "Then you can eat lunch, and you can come back to the piano and practice just before you go to the party."

"But Mom, I promised to play the "Happy Birthday" song and I can't even get through the first line!"

"See how you feel after you've rested and eaten," his mother said. "Sometimes that makes a difference."

"Okay," said Peter.

But, as he trudged off to his room to rest, he was not very hopeful.

Pretty soon it stopped raining. Peter woke from his nap and stared out of his window, feeling hopeless. All of a sudden a beautiful rainbow began to form.

As the rainbow became brighter and brighter, Peter got an idea! If he followed the rainbow and found the pot of gold at the end of it, he'd have enough money to buy the piano lesson he needed to play the song and maybe even enough to buy a new baby grand piano, like Suzy's.

Peter ran through the living room and out of the front door. His mother called to him from the kitchen, where she was making him a sandwich. "Peter, where are you going?"

"Don't worry, Mom!" Peter yelled, calling back to her while running for his bicycle. "I'm going to find the end of the rainbow. I'll be right back."

He reached his bicycle and jumped on, pedaling towards the rainbow, going as fast as he possibly could. He knew he had to hurry because rainbows don't last forever. Even though he didn't know exactly how to find the end of this one, he whizzed through the streets, determined to do it.

"Peter, Peter, wait..." It was Suzy, pedaling with all her might to catch up to him. "Wait for me!"

"I don't have much time!" Peter yelled.

"Where are you going?" asked Suzy.

"To find the end of the rainbow," Peter replied, as Suzy struggled to keep up with him. "I've got to hurry if I'm going to be able to play for your party," he explained.

"Great, then I'll go with you," said Suzy, excitedly.

Peter and Suzy pedaled as fast as they could toward the rainbow. Pretty soon they found themselves in an unfamiliar meadow at the edge of a deep, dark forest. They had some trouble finding their way into the forest, until they discovered a path they could follow.

Peter kept a lookout in the sky to make sure the rainbow was still there, and then they finally reached the trees. Peter jumped off of his bike, careful to look to his left and right so that he could spot some landmarks before going into the woods. He wanted to be sure they could find their way out again. Suzy rushed to catch up with him. She pointed at the rainbow and she was worried. "It's getting ahead of us!"

Suddenly Peter saw a bright pink rabbit munching on some strawberries. He said to Suzy, "That rabbit is turning pink from eating too many strawberries!" Just then the rabbit moved to a new set of berries. Peter thought he saw something strange in the foliage and sure enough, there was a purple pouch lying on the ground next to where the rabbit had just been. Embroidered on the top edge of the pouch was the partial arc of a rainbow. Below that, were the words, "The Rainbow Wizard's Magic Dust."

"Wow, maybe this can help us find the gold," said Peter. Suzy couldn't believe her eyes as she peered into the pouch. Lo and behold, inside the pouch was a bit of golden dust. Peter sprinkled some on the rabbit, who instantly grew four feet tall and said to the children, "Follow me! I'll help you get to the end of the rainbow!"

Whoosh! The pink rabbit was off and running into the woods. Peter and Suzy ran as fast as they could just to keep up with him.

Heading downhill, around a big boulder, they tumbled into another running figure—a golden-brown blur. Peter and Suzy crashed into the golden-brown blur and they all fell over. Dizzily the kids looked around and saw a big fuzzy bear. Suzy reached into the pouch and sprinkled the bear with the Wizard's magic dust. The bear laughed at their collision.

The kids told him, "We're heading for the end of the rainbow." Since no one was hurt, he decided to join them. "I'm going to get all the honey in the pot at the end of the rainbow!"

Peter and Suzy realized at once that Golden Bear had mistaken the gold at the end of the rainbow for honey! But when they saw the pink rabbit run off again into the distance, they had no time to explain. "Come with us!" they hollered to the bear, as they ran ahead after the rabbit.

The rainbow was beginning to fade when they reached the top of a tree-lined ridge. Peter and Suzy stared into the distance. They had lost the trail of Pinky Rabbit. "Well, I guess we might as well give up," said Peter. "It's almost time for the party."

"It's my birthday, and I say we keep trying," declared the birthday girl.

"Maybe we'll spot the rabbit from here," she continued, "but even if we can't find that rabbit, I know we'll find the end of the rainbow!"

"Wait... listen..." said Peter, as they both heard the "Happy Birthday" song being whistled, and it was echoing down the mountain. Someone else knew that it was Suzy's birthday!

"Look..." said Suzy, as she pointed to a bluebird that flew closer and closer as he continued to whistle the song.

Suzy opened the Wizard's pouch and sprinkled the bluebird with the magic dust.

"My name is Billy Bluebird," he chirped. "I want to help you have a wonderful birthday party!"

"Well..." said Peter, thoughtfully, "do you think you could fly ahead and sprinkle the last of the magic dust onto the rainbow? That would probably make it last longer so we could catch up to it!"

Billy Bluebird nodded his beak eagerly in agreement. He grabbed the strings of the pouch in his beak and flew at top speed in the direction of the fading rainbow. Peter and Suzy ran after him with Golden Bear right behind them. As Golden Bear struggled to keep up, he kept muttering, "Oh no, it's fading away and there goes my honey!"

Peter and Suzy and the creatures were almost out of breath when all of a sudden there was a brilliant flash of light and the rainbow became brighter than ever!

"This way," cried Pinky Rabbit, who had returned to lead them again. In moments they came to the rainbow's end. The sky glowed, alive with energy, and right there near the rainbow's edge was the pot of gold!

Golden Bear bounced up to the pot and put his nose inside. "Hey, there's no honey!" he exclaimed.

He was disappointed, but Peter put his arm around the unhappy bear and reassured him. "I will buy you all the honey you can eat. And, I'll buy all the seed you can eat too, Billy Bluebird. And for you, Pinky Rabbit, we'll fill a whole meadow with strawberries!"

Everyone laughed and danced around the pot of gold. But Peter suddenly spotted the empty Wizard's pouch lying nearby and remembered Suzy's party. "Darn," said Peter sadly, "we've used up all the magic dust and I still can't read the music notes to play for the party."

Suzy and the creatures stopped dancing. Suddenly all their joy was gone. They realized the time for the party was rapidly growing nearer.

Poof! A little Wizard, with a long golden beard and a rainbow on his hat, mysteriously appeared from behind the rainbow. He calmly walked over to Peter, who was holding the Wizard's pouch.

Of course Peter handed the pouch to the Wizard and sheepishly explained, "I was only trying to get the money for a piano lesson to play the "Happy Birthday" song and also to help my new friends."

"I know that," replied the Rainbow Wizard, which was his name.
He smiled and raised his arms towards the rainbow.
Colors began to stream from his fingertips.

He stretched and widened the rainbow until it had twelve colors instead of just seven; to fit over all the piano keys. Then he pointed his wand at each color and turned each one into a gold coin.

The coins fell at the Wizard's feet. He picked them up one by one, put them into the pouch and handed the pouch back to Peter.

"This will help you with your musical problem. Here's how to use them." The Rainbow Wizard bent down and whispered to Peter, whose eyes widened as he now understood what he must do next.

"C'mon, you're all invited to my birthday party!" exclaimed Suzy to the group. But just as suddenly as he had appeared, the Rainbow Wizard vanished!

Peter, Suzy, Pinky Rabbit, Golden Bear, and Billy Bluebird went back through the forest at top speed to where Peter and Suzy had left their bicycles. The kids led the creatures to Suzy's house, just in time for the birthday party.

Suzy's backyard had a beautiful party table, laid out next to a white baby grand piano. Streamers, balloons, and birthday bells in all the rainbow colors surrounded the yard. Peter's mother was there, helping Suzy's mother with the food. When everything was ready, everyone gathered at the table. Family, old friends, and new friends—were all together for Suzy's birthday party!

Peter sat down nervously at the piano and placed the gold coins on the music board above the black and white piano keys. Suzy's mother brought the cake to the table aglow with ten candles, one of which was for good luck!

It was a beautiful cake! Peter then whispered softly the magic saying that the Wizard had told him, ***"Believing is a dream come true."***

As he spoke the words, the gold coins burst apart and the colors inside them flew up onto the music sheet as colored music notes, and also flowed down onto the keyboard. Instantly, all the keys changed into colored keys. Now Peter could match the colored music notes to the colored piano keys! And that's just what he did as he now easily played the "Happy Birthday" song just right!

He played the "Happy Birthday" song the first time all alone on his color-keyed piano; but the second time through, everyone joined in singing to Suzy as she blew out the candles on her birthday cake and even still, the rainbow colors continued to glow.

The End

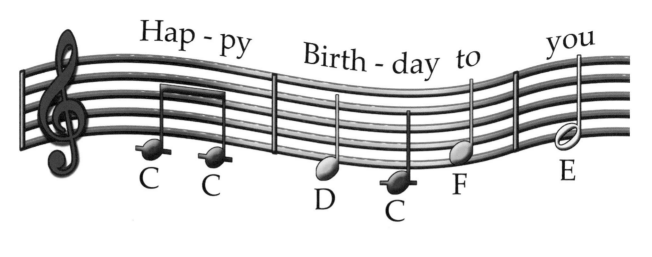

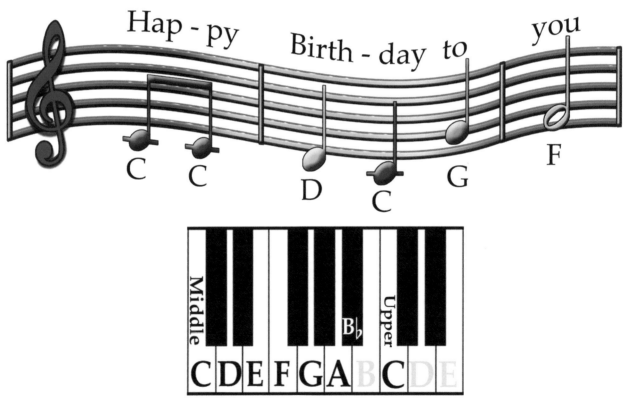

Use these lettered keys to play the song

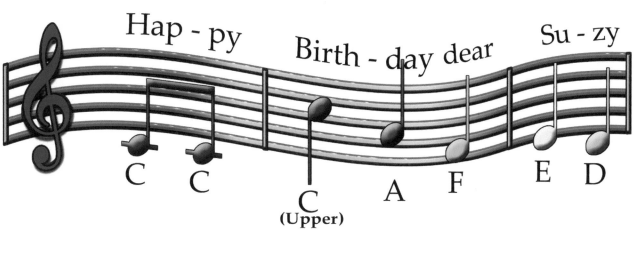

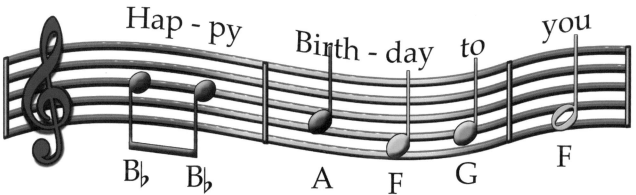

Use these lettered keys to play the song

The all important first step of your musical journey is locating the position of Middle C on the keyboard. Why? Because Middle C divides the keyboard in half. Above it are higher sounds. Below it are lower sounds.

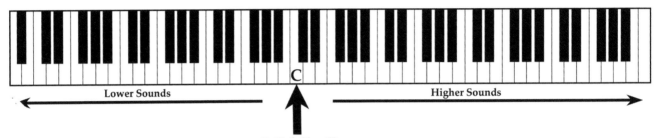

Lower Sounds ← → Higher Sounds

↑ Middle C

Middle C is in the very center of the keyboard.
Middle C is also the middle point, found between the 2 music staffs.

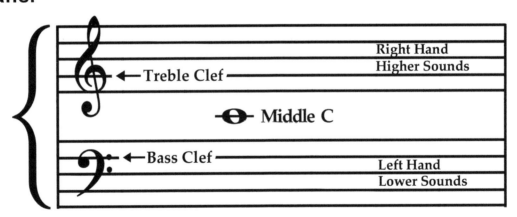

As you go above Middle C, (with the right hand) the sounds are higher.
As you go below Middle C, (with the left hand), the sounds are lower.

IMPORTANT! If you don't have a keyboard or piano, you may go online to play the Happy Birthday Song at: virtualpiano.net using your mouse or hotkeys to play the song.

Locating the C and F keys on the Keyboard

Being able to find your way around the piano keyboard is very important, here's a helpful way to get started.

When there is a group of 2 black keys, the key to the left of the 1st black key is *always a C key.*

When you see a group of 3 black keys, the key to the left of the 1st black key is *always an F key.*

Knowing how to find the C key is critical, because beginners' melodies are always placed in the key of C. This is because in the key of C there are no sharps or flats to be concerned about. You simply play on all the white keys. This makes it very easy to begin to play simple beginner melodies.

The music notes will be found on the lines and spaces of each staff and you play the keys associated with them to play a song. Each staff has 5 lines and 4 spaces.
The musical alphabet has only seven letters, A-B-C-D-E-F-G, that cover the white keys. (As you move in any direction, up or down, they keep repeating, in the same order.)

CPSIA information can be obtained at www.ICGtesting.com
Printed in the USA
LVIW01n0839170217
524597LV00002B/6